MW00358803

BUILDING
STIRLING ENGINES
WITHOUT A LATHE

by

Kjeld Hoejfeldt

Camden Miniature
Steam Services.

© KJELD HOEJFELDT 2004

All rights reserved. No part of this publication may be reproduced, stored in a retrieval system, or transmitted in any form or by any means, electronic, mechanical, photocopying, recording or otherwise without prior permission in writing from the publishers.

Kjeld Hoejfeldt asserts the moral right as the author of this work.

British Library Cataloguing-in-Publication-Data: a catalogue record of this book is held by the British Library.

First Printing 2004
Second Printing 2006

ISBN No. 0-9547131-0-9

Published in Great Britain by:

CAMDEN MINIATURE STEAM SERVICES
Barrow Farm, Rode, Frome, Somerset. BA11 6PS
www.camdenmin.co.uk

Camden stock one of the widest selections of engineering, technical and hot air engine books to be found; Contact them at the above address for a copy of their latest free Booklist.

Layout and design by Camden Studios.

Printed by Salisbury Printing Co. Ltd.

IMPORTANT:
the construction of the models in this book, and the running of them, can potentially be hazardous. The author and publisher are just passing on information - your safety, and that of others, is entirely your responsibility.

CONTENTS

INTRODUCTION

Why this little book?

First of all I should like to encourage more people to take an interest in the Stirling engine, not only because it is exciting but also because this engine can help us to a better use of our resources and so to live in a better environment. Even if you are not a technically educated person, it is a good thing to be aware of different developments concerning the use of energy and what happens when political decisions are taken. The internet is a splendid source of information for this.

The other reason is that I like the engines very much and I think that the best way to get an idea of what a Stirling engine really is, and how it works, is to build one yourself.

You can build a very simple Stirling engine without spending money (or only a little, anyway) and are likely to find it so interesting that you will go on to build other more complicated models.

Here we can run into problems because not all of us have the space or money for a fine workshop and a lathe, usually regarded as a necessity when building model engines.

I ran into the same problems but I continued in my small workshop by using mainly different scrap materials. As far as "how to do it" is concerned, I tried to find out myself and, as an encouragement, I should mention that I am not an engineer but a chartered accountant by profession.

I still have no lathe. It is a challenge but challenges are there to be overcome and they have given me many exciting hours.

Apart from Chapter 1 in which detailed building instructions are given, Chapters 2, 3 and 4 are mainly descriptions of the engines I have built, with less detail, but including general advice.

Chapter 5, concerning Stirling engines past and present, is of no particular relevence as far as building Stirling model engines goes, but I felt that the models would probably give rise to many questions about this old engine (patented in 1816) and the future in store for it. Therefore I felt it to be suitable to include a little information from its long and fascinating story.

I hope that you will get pleasure in reading this book. For me it has been a pleasure to write it because, among other things, I have experienced that many people including members of modelling or technical clubs have been very interested in the engines.

Last but not least, many thanks to my friend Henning Moeller from the Danish Inventors Association for going through the manuscript and for his advice, and to Andy Ross, *Victron Energy*, *Kockums* and *NASA* for their help in providing illustrations and information.

Copenhagen February 2004

Kjeld Hoejfeldt

CHAPTER 1

THE CAN STIRLING – MODEL NO. 1

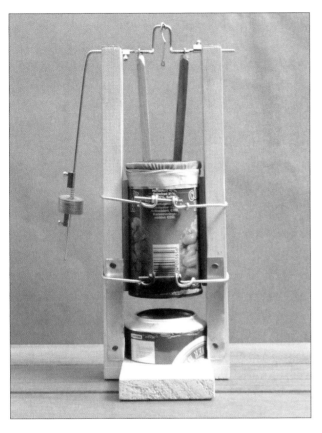

Fig. 1.1

The Can Stirling engine is, like the first engine the inventor, Robert Stirling, patented in 1816, equipped with one cylinder and two pistons. Such engines are nowadays called "Beta Configurations".

The Can Stirling is the most simple and inexpensive engine you can build. A good engine can perform 100 to 300 revolutions per minute, can give you hours of fun and a good time to share with your friends who will be highly surprised.

I got the inspiration for my kind of Can Stirlings from the internet, but I don´t know who the originator of this simple engine was and when he made his first one.

Now please study the picture Fig. 1.1 and let's get to work.

ENGINE CONSTRUCTION

An important part of the engine is the frame (Fig. 1.2). This can be made in various ways out of metal or wood. I made my rest from a board 40 cms in length, 6.7 cms wide, and 1.5 cms thick.

Using my saw I cut off 15 cms for the wooden base and from the surplus I made two pillars 1.5 x 3.3 x 25 cms.

Then I drilled two holes in the pillars and fastened them to the wooden base with two screws.

On top of the pillars I made a groove which is 3 millimetres in depth. These grooves are the bearings for the crankshaft and in order

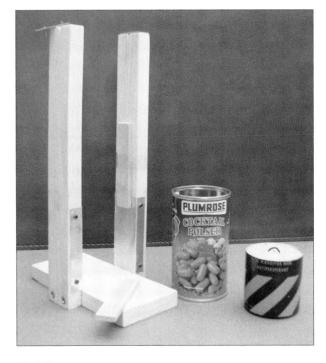

Fig. 1.2

to keep the crankshaft in position, the top of the pillars are provided with two small plates held with two screws. These plates are made from a plastic lid.

The pillars are partly covered with metal plates to protect them from heat. The metal plates are cut out of a beer can and they are glued to the pillars and held in place with four small nails.

The can you can see in the centre of Fig. 1.2 is 10 cms high and the diameter is 5.9 cms. This can is the part of the engine called the displacer cylinder. Later the open top of the can will be provided with a rubber diaphragm.

When you erect the can between the pillars you will need two spacers to keep the can central. These are shown in Fig. 1.2 and one of them can be seen situated in the correct position by the pillar.

The part of a black aerosol tin (cut off with a little hacksaw) on the right of the displacer cylinder in Fig. 1.2 is the displacer piston. This is 5.3 cms high and the diameter is also 5.3 cms.

The task of this piston is to transfer the air inside the can from one end to the other. When the displacer piston is at its upper level the air is at the hot (bottom) end of the cylinder. Here the air expands driving the diaphragm (the power piston) upwards. When the displacer piston returns to its lower level the air is transferred around it (there are some millimetres between the piston and the cylinder wall) to the cold end of the displacer cylinder where the air again contracts. This changing of temperature drives the engine and is a very fast process.

The displacer piston has been fitted with a wooden lid about 1 cm thick (balsa wood

is preferable). It is glued to the inner piston wall with a fast-acting glue. It is also recommended to fix the lid using two nails or with some extra glue at the edge of the tin. Make this as airtight as you can.

Before assembly, the centre of the lid has to be fitted with a little shackle for a thin nylon fishing line. The shackle is half a paper-clip.This is pressed through the centre of the lid and the points are then bent back and kept in place with blobs of glue.

Now to a little more ingenious work. We have to bend a steel wire 32 cms long and at least 2.3 mms thick to form a crank. A wire clothes-hanger from a dry cleaners is ideal. In any case it is important that the crank is stiff and not flexible.

To do the job you need one or two pairs of pliers of about 5 to 6 mms across the jaws (and your hands, of course).

Look at Fig. 1.3, and begin to work bending the wire into a right angle 3.5 cms from the beginning of the wire. After that bend another right angle 9 mms from the first. The distance of 9 mms and all other distances will be measured here from the centre of the wire.

Continue the work following the instructions and the measurements stated in the picture. Some problems will

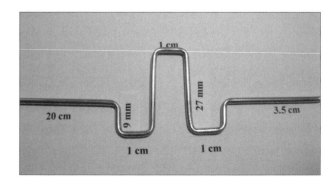

Fig. 1.3

probably arise and inaccuracies appear. Such deviations can create problems later on; therefore it is recommended to correct them while work is in progress.

In the design of a Stirling engine, as a starting point, there should be a angle of 90 degrees between the throw of the displacer piston and the throw of the power piston. To create this, bend the middle of the crank into a 90 degree as shown in Fig.1.4.

Then lay the crankshaft into the grooves on top of the pillars and turn the crankshaft to check your work. Any inaccuracies should be corrected; you will be rewarded for a good crankshaft later on .

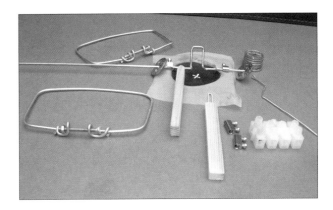

Fig. 1.5

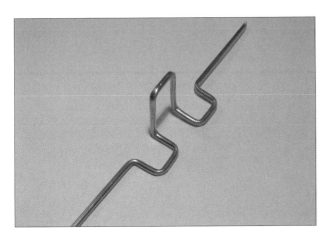

Fig. 1.4

Now we have to start making the smaller parts of the engine.

In Fig 1.5 you can see the diaphragm. It is a piece (10 x 10 cms) cut from a pair of thin rubber gloves or a big toy balloon. The diaphragm is provided with a thin leather patch (diameter 4.5 cms) on both sides.

The leather patches are glued to the diaphragm with a contact adhesive. The diaphragm is provided with two holes for the screws for the connecting rods. You will have to cut or burn these holes. The distance between the holes should be 2.6 cms (i.e. each hole is situated 1.3 cms from the centre).

Finally, using a needle, thread 15 cms of thin nylon fishing line with a total length of 30 cms through the centre of the patches.

In Fig. 1.5 the crank can be seen and one of the connecting rods, made of wood is shown mounted to the crank. The rods are 0.6 x 1.0 cm and the length is 8.0 cms. They are connected to the crank by a little staple. The staple is easy to make out of a straightened paperclip. Bend the clip on the crankshaft and then cut off the points measuring 1 cm or a little more.

Next prick two small holes in the top of the connecting rod and hammer the staple into the rod leaving about 2.5 mms for the crank.

To avoid problems with the engine's operation, cut off the superfluous wood at the top of the connecting rod close to the staple.

We also need three electric connectors without their plastic insulation. Two are to secure the balance weight on the fly arm and one, cut in two halves with a little hacksaw, is for making two spacers between the pillars and the crank.

For the fishing line we need some steel wire (straightened paper clip again) 6 to 8 cms in length. Form a little eye at the end of the wire and then bend the wire into a **Z** shape about 2 cms from the eye.

To hold the can (displacer cylinder) between the pillars we need two *Jubilee Clips*. You can either buy these, or make them yourself out of steel wire and a nut and bolt.

ASSEMBLING THE ENGINE

So far so good. We have now reached the stage of assembling all the parts we have made.

Let´s begin with a look at the complete engine (Fig.1.1) and consider what we should do first.

1. Pass one of the ends of the fishing line from the diaphragm through the shackle on the lid of the displacer piston, and make a knot. It is recommended to make a *Fishermans Knot* as shown.

2. Pass the other end of the fishing line through the eye of the **Z** wire and make 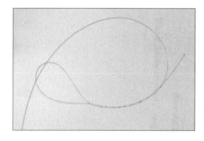 a knot in the eye when the length of the line between the shackle and the eye is 6 to 7 cms.

3. Fasten the connecting rods to the diaphragm with a little screw.

4. Put the displacer piston into the can.

5. Attach electrical tape to the top and open edge of the can to protect the diaphragm from direct heat from the metal wall.

6. Place the diaphragm on the top of the can and fasten the edges with some small pieces of paper tape so that the centre of the diaphragm is situated above the centre of the can. When the diaphragm is straightened but not stretched, put a loose rubber band around the diaphragm skirt and correct the position of the diaphragm or other deviations. Then put one or two rubber bands tight around the skirt close to the top of the can.

Now the can (displacer cylinder), the connecting rods, and the crank have been assembled. Cut any superfluous material off the diaphragm and cover the remainder with a strip of paper tape.

7. Put the two halves of the connector on each end of the crank and lay the crankshaft into the grooves on top of the pillars. Put the two small plastic plates onto the grooves and fasten them with four small screws.

8. Grip the long part of the crankshaft with a pair of pliers close to the pillar and, using your hand, bend the extension downwards, making sure the crank is pointing upwards. We have now made the fly arm.

9. Put the *Jubilee Clips* around the pillars. Tighten them a little and place the wooden spacers on the inner side of the pillars. Next move the can upwards until the diaphragm is flat and the middle of the crank is point-ing upwards. Then tighten the *Jubilee Clips*, but not too hard.

10. Now back again to the **Z** wire with the fishing line. You should lace up the wire to the middle of the crank. It is an important part of the mounting because the displacer piston should not hit the bottom of the can when the piston is at its lowest level or touch the diaphragm when it is at its highest level. If either problem does arise you can solve it by making the **Z** wire a little longer or shorter by changing the bendings.

11. Fasten one of the connectors on the fly arm 10 cms from the crankshaft. Put the weight (for example some metal washers with a weight of around 25 grammes) on the fly arm and secure them with the other connector.

12. Make a furnace. This could be, for example, 3 to 4 cms cut off the lower part of a beer can.

13. Grease the fishing line and the hole in the centre of the diaphragm and oil all the bearings. Oiling every time you run the engine is important - but do not over oil.

14. Put a piece of solid alchohol fuel in the furnace but no more than one gram. This is the safest fuel. You can also use other fuels, but the heat from a candle is probably not strong enough this model.

RUNNING THE ENGINE

Now we have come to the most exciting event; the very first run of the engine.

Light the fuel and hold the base of the engine down with your hand or a clamp, because the fly arm makes the engine bounce when it starts revolving.

Now wait and see. Within 15 seconds the diaphragm begins to bulge and the engine is ready.

Give the engine a little help by turning the fly arm. You will soon find out which way the engine wants to revolve.

It would be unusual if there was nothing to be adjusted now.

It could be that the can has to be moved a little upwards or downwards or the weight on the fly arm is situated a little too high or too low.

The position of the weight, together with the level of the heating, will determine the speed of the engine.

Perhaps you might also have to adjust the **Z** wire, or the heating

Anyway, you are sure to succeed in the end.

Good luck and take care of the engine. DO NOT OVERHEAT IT; this will damage the diaphragm.

PLEASE NOTE that the dimensions given in this chapter, and those that follow, are based on the materials I had available, and will need to be adjusted if you use different items for certain parts; for example, if you use a different size can for the displacer cylinder. However most cans nowadays are standard sizes and it should not be too difficult to find the same sizes I used to build the models.

As long as you understand the concepts involved, then varying the dimensions for your engines should not be difficult.

For your design of Tin Can Stirling Engine:

CHAPTER 2

THE WORKSHOP AND MATERIALS

THE WORKSHOP

You can make Model No. 1 at a kitchen work-top using the tools mentioned in Chapter 1. For making more advanced models though (for example those made of metal) you need a workshop and more tools. However, if you do have to create a workshop for model building, it will also be useful for repairing a lot of other things around your home.

First of all you need a workbench with a vice. This vice should not be too small. After that it is recommended to get a wood saw and a large and a small metal saw (hacksaws). You will also need some pliers, spanners, files and screwdrivers with bits and heads of different sizes and types. When breaking up scrapped small machines you will be surprised how many kinds and sizes of bolts and screws there are.

An electric soldering iron is often required when making parts out of brass or copper, and a power drill with drills of different sizes, suitable for drilling metal, and a rotating rubber disc for sandpaper, is also necessary.

On the whole the purchase price is a question of quality. That's why you can often buy, for example, a whole assortment of screwdrivers at the same price as that of a single, good quality, one.

Even if some of the cheap tools are usable and sometimes good to have, you will soon find out the difference between a good file and a bad one. The quantity and the quality of tools in your workshop will depend upon your wishes and your purse, of course, but it is quite possible to assemble an adequate range of tools without spending a fortune.

Later on you will probably want to increase your selection of tools. A bench power drill is much better than a hand-held power drill. You can buy them very cheaply nowadays; machines imported from China, for example, are perfectly adequate for non-professionals, although it is always wise to check their accuracy before using them for the first time.

The need for a kind of a Gas Blow Torch for silver soldering will also probably arise within the foreseeable future, and these can be bought from D-I-Y stores.

There are no limits to the size of workshop and the amount of tools and accessories you have, but remember there should be no hurry for beginners to increase their facilities. It is more important that you learn and gain experience by making things and handling the tools before rushing to expand.

THE MATERIALS

Everybody will know the situation where you just need a screw, a small metal plate or a piece of wood but you can't find what you want. This can present a serious practical problem so it is, therefore, very important for anyone starting model making to build up a good stock of materials.

But how?

You can buy small nuts and bolts, metal sheet, bars and brass tubes but it will never be sufficient for your projects. Many of the other things you need will often be rather hard to find or too expensive to buy. Therefore acquire your materials "from the world of scrap" like most hobby people do. This can prove a good source for more than just raw materials such as metal sheet and bars. You can also find some useful and interesting material by breaking up old scrapped radios, gramophones, printers, video players, reel tape-recorders, computers and other miscellaneous items you have been given, or have discovered.

Part of a yield is shown in Fig. 2.1.

It is very exciting and there are endless possibilities: ball bearings from a computer hard disc, flywheels, ball bearings, brass bearings from video players, gramophones or tape recorders; steel shafts and small electric engines from Audio or CD drives, cooling fins, nuts and bolts from a radio, and sheet metal from all sorts of things. You will come across random items with no apparent use, all over the place, but one day these things may be exactly what you need to continue your project or to give you inspiration when you hold them in your hands. It is funny but sometimes it is a good idea to try to think with your hands.

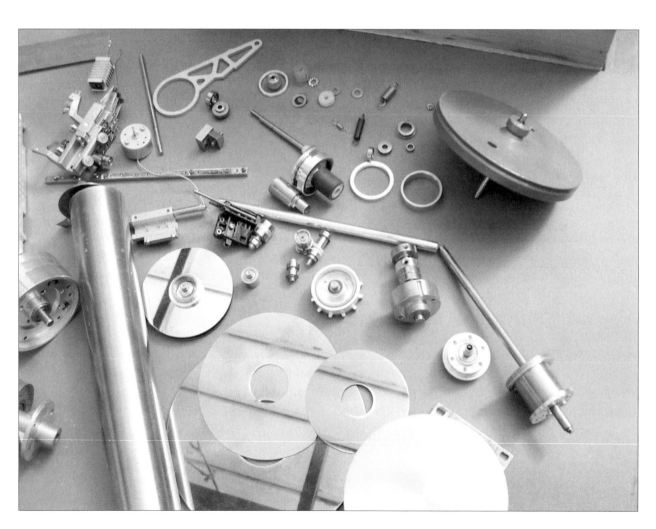

Fig. 2.1

CHAPTER 3

MORE CAN STIRLING EXPERIMENTS

After making model No.1, I thought that using a flywheel would make a better engine. This turned out to be true and afterwards I made three such engines. In this chapter the engines will be presented one by one. Descriptions of the engines and some advice are included but, unlike Chapter 1, there are no detailed building instructions because these engines were mainly constructed from different scrap I had available in my stock.

Now you must judge my engines and make better ones yourself. I hope that they will give you a lot of ideas and help you to succeed.

Can Stirling Engine with a Flywheel from a Reel Tape Recorder – Model No. 2:

This engine was my first one fitted with a flywheel. In my stock I found a wheel 10 cms in diameter. It came from an old tape recorder and it was rather heavy. A part of the base including the bearing was also available from my supplies. Then the task, among many others, was to make a frame and fit the base of the bearing to this. This will be described, but first of all two photographs of the completed engine are shown below.

In Fig. 3.1.1 the engine is shown from the front. The construction of the engine is, in many ways, similar to engine No.1 in Chapter 1, and the can, the displacer piston and the diaphragm have the same measurements. The obvious differences are the flywheel, the crank, and the frame of course. The frame is 24 cms high and,

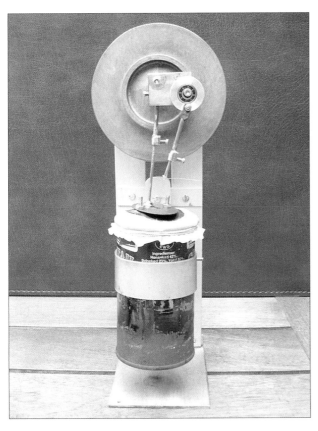

Fig. 3.1.1

Fig. 3.1.2

including the top of the flywheel, the engine is 26 cms in height.

In Figs. 3.1.2 & 3.1.3 you can see the crank and two connecting rods. The rod next to the flywheel is the connecting rod to the diaphragm and the outer one is that of the displacer piston. To equalise the total weight of the crank and the connecting rods, the other end of the crankshaft is provided with a weight for counter-balancing.

The frame and the clamp around the can are made from aluminium sheet and is 25 mms wide and 2.6 mms thick. The base is cut from the chassis of an old radio. In Fig. 3.1.1 and Fig. 3.1.2 you can see the design of the frame.

Now to the important parts of the engine: the crank and the connecting rods. They are shown in Fig. 3.1.3 and Fig. 3.1.4.

The two crank webs (30 mms x 22 mms and 1.5 mms thick) are made of brass. (A web is an arm or a disc in the crank). A bush with a bolt has been soldered onto the web nearest the flywheel. This bush is mounted to the crankshaft and held by the bolt.

A hole has been drilled in the web 9 mms from the centre of the bush and a short piece of a copper tube (3 mms in diameter) has been placed in the hole. The copper tube is the crank for the connecting rod to the diaphragm. Afterwards the copper tube is fixed to the web by soldering and then fitted with a small ball-bearing.

A hole has also been drilled in the other web to fit it to the first web and the copper tube. The copper tube has then been fixed to this web by soldering. Soft-soldering was used, but has proved durable.

The distance between the two webs is 4.75

Fig. 3.1.3   *Fig. 3.1.4*

mms. It is recommended when soldering to put a wooden distance piece between the webs to keep them the correct distance apart, and to keep the first soldered joint cool. It will also help if you use a lower temperature solder for this joint.

To mount the connecting rod of the displacer piston, the outer side of the web should be provided with a pin 18 mms from the centre of the crankshaft and at a right angle to the copper tube crank. On an impulse, however, instead of that, I mounted a ball-bearing with a collar made of aluminium. A nice little thing from a hard disc in my stock.

This is how the two cranks needed for the engine were made. The first one has a throw of 9 mms and the second one has a throw of 18 mms (equal to the specifications of model No.1).

Finally I cut off the superfluous part of the copper tube outside the web to avoid problems with the distance between the outer ball bearing and the web. I didn't cut the webs into the shape of the letter L (a bell crank) because the rectangular web and the circular collar are fundamentally geometric shapes which suit each other here.

In Fig. 3.1.3 and Fig. 3.1.4 you can also see the connecting rods. These are made of a piece of a copper tube (3 mms in outer diameter) and a piece of a brass tube (2 mms in outer diameter). This brass tube fits well within the inner diameter of the copper tube. The brass tube is attached to the copper tube by a muff soldered to the copper tube. In this way it is very easy to adjust the length of the connecting rods.

The connecting rod to the diaphragm has been soldered to a small copper plate mounted on the diaphragm. The other end

of the rod has been connected to a small copper strip bent around the ball bearing on the crank and provided with a small bolt and a nut.

This engine revolves much better than model No.1 but not very fast. I think that is because the diameter of the flywheel is too small, so I equipped the next engine with a very large flywheel. Why not?

Can Stirling Engine with a Flywheel from a Gramophone – Model No.3:

I made this engine just for fun and to get an idea of how powerful these Can Stirling Engines could be.

The diameter of the flywheel is 26 cms and it is rather a heavy one for this small engine. The engine, however, seems to like the flywheel and it makes enough power to

Fig. 3.2.1

Fig. 3.2.2

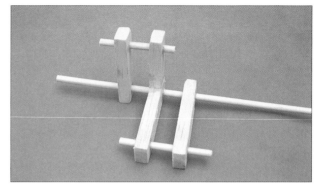

Fig. 3.2.3

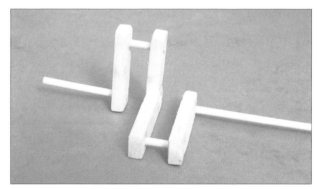

Fig. 3.2.4

turn it. The engine starts a little slowly but after a while it builds up to 200 RPM. In my opinion, therefore, Can Engines are quite powerful.

The other improvement on this engine, apart from the flywheel, is the crank shown in Fig. 3.2.2.

It can be rather difficult to make cranks; a good way to make one is shown here, by a wooden model, in Fig. 3.2.3 and Fig. 3.2.4.

As you can see, to keep the assembly rigid, the cranks are built-up on the uncut crankshaft, as this avoids many problems, especially if the crank has many webs.

When the relevant parts of the crank have been fixed by soldering or by using a metal glue, you can cut off the surplus rods and the result is shown in Fig. 3.2.4.

The wooden crank shown has the same appearance as the crank of the engine described in this section. A close-up of the crank is shown in Fig. 3.2.5.

On the left you can see a spacer on the end of the crankshaft. To the right of this a brass bush is screwed to the shaft, and one web is soldered to the brass bush.

Fig. 3.2.5

A hole has been made in this web 9 mms from the centre of the bush and a short copper tube has been soldered into this hole. A bearing bush with a hole in its centre rotates on this tube. The connecting rod of the diaphragm is mounted in this hole and soldered in place.

The next web, again soldered to the copper tube just mentioned, has the shape of the letter L (a bell crank), to fulfil the need for an angle of 90 degrees between the throw of the displacer piston and the throw of the power piston.

The legs of the bell crank are respectively 17 and 27 mms and provided with two holes respectively 9 and 18 mms from the hole situated in the angle of the web.

The short leg of the bell crank is connected with, and soldered to, the copper tube in the first web and the long leg is, in the same way, connected to the third web situated to the right and so on.

The frame of the engine isn't complicated, so a full description is not needed. The only important things are the two pieces of brass bar mounted on the pillars above the displacer cylinder (Fig. 3.2.1 and Fig. 3.2.5). The purpose of these bars is, together with the two threaded distance rods and two nuts, to adjust the pressure of the pillars against the can.

The black base is a cover from a hard disc.

Can Stirling Engine with a Fan – Model No. 4:

I felt that the Can Stirlings deserved better presentation, and that the models ought to be made more carefully of better materials. At the same time I thought that better design and good workmanship

would reduce the friction and also the heat required. Perhaps this would also extend the lifetime of the diaphragm.

The next engine I made, shown in Fig. 3.3.1 and Fig. 3.3.2, I called "Salute to Can".

The design of the frame looks very simple, and it is - it is just one pillar made from Brazilian rosewood. It is 44 cms high and it comes from a leg of a scrapped table. The base is also very simple. It is a heavy wheel made of brass and it seems to have been a part of some big machine.

The fan that serves as the flywheel is shown in Fig. 3.3.3 lying in a wooden bed. The fan is made of circular copper plates 10 cms in diameter soldered to brass tubes with a diameter of 4 mms. The length of the tubes is 10 cms. The centre hub of the fan, also

Fig. 3.3.1

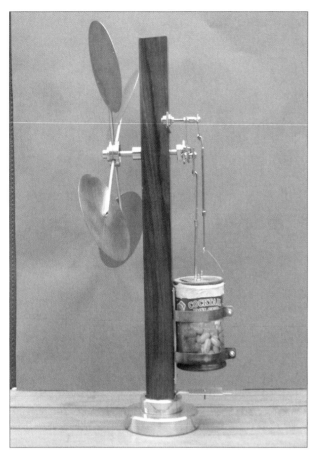

Fig. 3.3.2

made of brass, was part of a fast speed rotating wheel inside a video recorder.

The purpose of the wooden bed is to keep the single parts of the fan in their correct positions when soldering. As you can see wooden wedges were used to keep the fan blades in the right position. You will also see that one of the fan blades is provided

Fig. 3.3.3

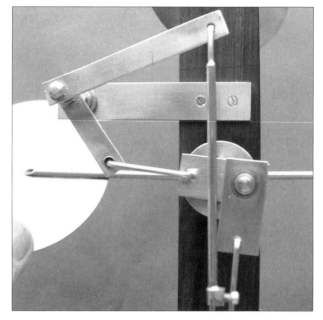

Fig. 3.3.4

Fig. 3.3.5

with some strips of paper tape. They make a barrier to prevent the molten solder spreading.

In Fig. 3.3.4 you see the crank mechanism in its highest position, and in Fig. 3.3.5 it is in the lowest position.

This design of crank mechanism is a lever / linkage one. It works well and is very interesting to watch. In Fig. 3.3.6 a close-up shows the linkage from above.

In Fig. 3.3.6 you can also see that a hole has been drilled through the pillar. Each end

Fig. 3.3.6

has been fitted with a ball-bearing, which is fitted to the shaft of the fan. The shaft at the opposite end of the fan has been equipped with a bush made of brass. Part of this bush has been cut off, using a file, to make room for the bolt of the disc pin.

The crank disc is fastened to the bush by two bolts. I made the disc myself by mounting a rough off-cut from a brass bar on a shaft and then putting the shaft in a power drill held by a vice. While this was rotating the superfluous brass was removed by pressing a file quite hard against the rotating surface.

(I have done this several times but **don't do it yourself. It is dangerous.** The power drill and the file have to be well supported and you have to take extreme care of your fingers.)

The brass angle, also shown from the front in Fig. 3.3.4 and Fig. 3.3.5, is a part of the mechanism which gives the gap of 90 degrees between the throw of the displacer piston and that of the power piston. The angle consists of two pieces of brass soldered to a spacer (a brass tube).

The length of the long leg of the angle is twice the length of the short leg because the displacer piston in this engine (and the previous engines) moves 18 mms up and down while the diaphragm, in the same way, moves just 9 mms.

The lengths of the movements, however, are not only dependent on that of the legs of the angle. They are also decided by the length of the radius from the centre of the crank-shaft to the centre of the disc pin.

If the radius mentioned is 9 mms, the disc pin will move the connecting rod of the diaphragm 9 mms up and down. As the disc pin is also connected to the short leg of the angle this will, at the same time, cause the short leg to be moved 9 mms to the right and to the left, and the long leg, connected to the connecting rod of the displacer piston, to be moved 18 mms upwards and downwards.

The angle has a shaft. This passes through the spacer and is then mounted in a double ball bearing (from a hard disc) fixed to the piece of a brass bar screwed to the frame.

The connecting rods are similar to the rods shown in the previous sections but they are much longer and each of them has been soldered to a rectangular piece of brass. This is to make space for mounting the ball bearings of the disc pin.

The design of the drive mechanism mentioned above did, of course, give rise to some mathematical challenges whilst building the engine; however that is unavoidable and is a stimulating part of building the model.

I didn't make calculations or drawings before the beginning of the job. Building this engine, and the other engines as well, I just began with some ideas. Some of them were good and some of them turned out to be wrong. When problems do occur they always involve changing the plans, and demand that you do some specific drawings and calculations while work is actually in progress.

As far as the improvements to the engine are concerned, I am very pleased with the results. Using just a candle as the heat source, the engine revolves at more than 100 RPM - making a mild breeze - for two hours, and it has done this many times. Using solid fuel, the engine revolves at up to 300 RPM.

The displacer cylinder hasn't been changed to a very fine one. The can has been retained to remain true to the original concept and to make a contrast to the other much better materials used in this case.

For your design of Tin Can Stirling Engine:

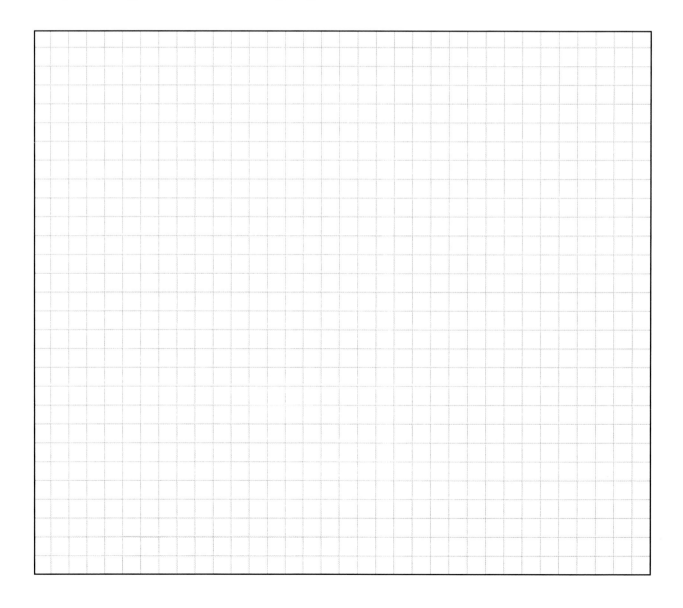

Chapter 4

Stirling Engines – the Gamma Configuration

The difference between the Beta configuration described in Chapter 1 and the Gamma configuration described in this chapter is that Gamma engines are not only provided with one cylinder but with two - a power cylinder and a displacer cylinder.

When I was building my first Can Stirling I felt that I needed the experience of a real model engine. On the Internet I found a model manufactured by *P.M. Research, Inc.* at a reasonable purchase price, which included a very good book by Andy Ross. This engine performs up to 1000 RPM and it demonstrates the Gamma configuration very well. It is shown in Fig. 4.

The small cylinder is the power cylinder, like the one you know from a model steam engine.

The difference is that the piston is not powered by a steam boiler but by a displacer (here provided with cooling fins as you can see in the upper part of the picture) which is linked by a tube to the cylinder, in this case on the left of the plate connecting the two cylinders.

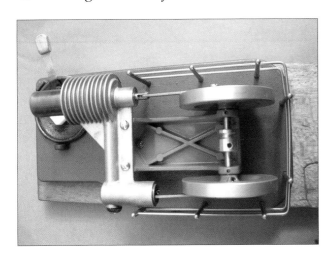

Fig. 4

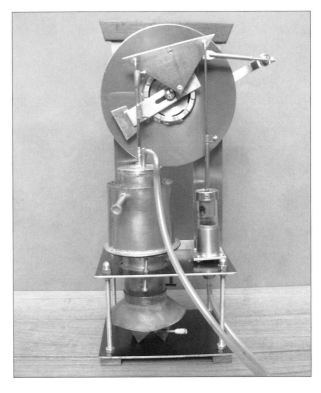

Fig. 4.1.1

**Gamma Stirling Engine
with Ross Linkage – Model No. 5:**

My first engine fitted with separate cylinders (a Gamma configuration) is shown below in Fig. 4.1.1 and Fig. 4.1.2. The engine is 31 cms high and it is made mainly of brass and copper. The design looks a little complicated but in reality it is not.

The flywheel and the bearing come from an old hard disc. The diameter of the flywheel is 13 centimetres and it is fitted with an adjustable crank pin. The most exciting thing is the Ross linkage (patented by Andy Ross) mounted on the crank pin. It causes the connecting rods to move only very slightly to the sides, and a coupling block is therefore not needed, as the cylinders can also move a little. The workings of the Ross linkage are shown in Figs. 4.1.3 & 4.1.4.

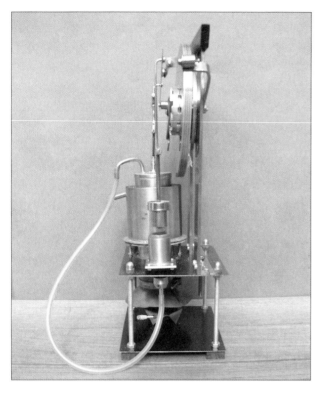

Fig. 4.1.1

As you can see the angle is, in a way, standing upon the crank pin; therefore it moves up and down following the revolution of the crank pin. However, as the upper part of the angle is held in place by a rod connected to a bearing and is fastened to the frame of the engine at the other end, the angle is also forced to make a rocking movement. This causes the connecting rod of the displacer to move up and down thereby changing the pressure. On the other hand, the connecting rod of the power piston, supplied with power from the power piston, moves the angle up and down and so makes the flywheel revolve.

The Ross linkage fulfils the demand for a angle between the movement of the two connecting rods very well. It works efficiently and is frequently used in Stirling engines. It is also very interesting to watch.

The power cylinder is part of the body of a syringe cut off and placed in a short length of copper tube soldered to a square of brass. Here it has been fixed by a little epoxy repair-sealer. The brass tube from the bottom of power cylinder, which goes through the base, and over which the plastic tube to the displacer cylinder slides, is fitted with two buffers made of rubber. One fits above and one below the base to allow the power cylinder a small rocking movement. The tube is held below the lower buffer by a bush with a bolt.

The inner diameter of the power cylinder is 15.7 mms and the piston which fits to the cylinder wall is made of steel. I thought that is was a good idea to grease the cylinder wall a little but this was wrong. The cylinder and the piston must be kept clean. The displacer cylinder is made of brass and

Fig. 4.1.3

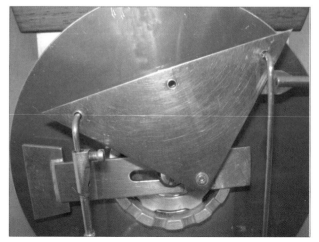

Fig. 4.1.4

cut off a weight cover which originally came from a wall clock. The inner diameter is 39 mms and the cylinder is 127 mms high. The bottom cover is silver-soldered onto the cylinder because of the heat which is applied there to run the engine, whilst the upper cover is soft soldered. As well as a screen to protect the upper base against heat, the cylinder is provided with an annular water cooler to keep the upper part of the cylinder comparatively cold.

The displacer piston is made of aluminium and it is a kind of medical container. The diameter of this is 36.9 mms and the length is 90.5 mms. Compared with the height of the cylinder (127 mms) it allows a movement of 36.5 millimetres inside the cylinder.

The displacer cylinder is not fastened to the base. It is only resting, held by its own weight, onto the top of two bolts. This is adequate because even if there alternately is high and low pressure inside the cylinder there is always the same pressure above and below the displacer piston and, thus, if the speed does not exceed a certain limit, there is no resistance to the movements of the piston in this engine.

Parts of the engine are shown in Fig. 4.1.5

The engine described in this section works well and can run at more than 500 RPM.

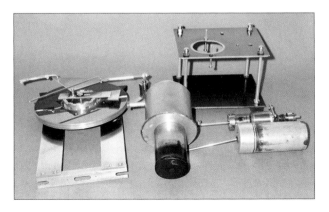

Fig. 4.1.5

Unfortunately a little accident occurred inside the displacer cylinder and at the time the pictures shown in this section were taken, the engine was under repair. That is why the plastic tube between the cylinders is temporary and too long. The guide bush on top of the displacer cylinder is also temporary. The guide bush has to fit well to the piston rod to ensure that no air escapes from inside the cylinder, but not so tight that it causes too much friction. If the pressurised air can escape easily from the cylinder the engine certainly will not work, but if there is only a very small leak, the engine can be got working because, as the air inside the cylinder cools and contracts, it will suck some air back.

In this case the displacer piston rod is made of steel, and the top of the guide bush is made of bronze or brass, both coming from an A-drive of a presinal computer. Some engines work better with the piston rod lubricated, but others work better dry - you will have to see. If you do oil your engine, use a light oil such as for sewing machines.

I called this engine "China" because I thought that it had a Chinese look. This wasn't intentional but sometimes it happens. You think you are designing the engines but once you start, they seem to take over and design themselves.

Low Temperature Differential Stirling Engine (LTD) – Model No. 6:

These engines are of more recent origin and were developed from the beginning of 1980 by Professor Ivo Kolin of Zagreb, Croatia. He succeeded quite early on in getting a Stirling engine to revolve with only a difference of 20 degrees Celcius between the hot end and the cold end of the displacer cylinder. Later on Prof. James R

Senft, U.S.A. developed LTD engines with a difference as low as 0.5 degree C.

The engines are characterised by a very thin but very wide displacer cylinder. The heating requirement is low, of course, and it often comes from just hot water.

They are highly suitable for educational purposes because you can watch both of the pistons when the engine is working. Perhaps further developments of large LTD engines will also give these engines a place in the field of energy production, although so far none have been built which develop any useable power.

An LTD engine complete with drawings and building instructions was the first engine I saw on the Internet but, at that time, I found it too difficult to make. Later on I became very curious about these engines and their extremely low heating requirements. One day I decided to make a simple displacer just out of material available in my stock.

The engine was only intended to be experimental. That is why the copper plates are rectangular and have not been made circular. After all, why use any more time than necessary on things which probably

won't work? However I succeeded much better than I imagined possible and the engine now revolves rather satisfactorily. It was not as difficult to build an LTD engine as I thought.

The engine is shown in Figs. 4.2.1 & 4.2.2.

The base of the engine consists of two copper plates 11 x 17.5 cms and 1.85 mms thick. (Aluminium plate 3 mms thick is better and is recommended).

The displacer cylinder is situated between the copper plates and fastened by eight nuts and bolts fitted around the outside the cylinder wall. The inner diameter of this cylinder is 90 mms and it is 22 mms high including the rubber seals. It was very carefully cut from a sugar container found in the kitchen, to ensure the top and bottom edges were parallel.

As with the other engines, the displacer cylinder needs to be airtight. It was too difficult for me to make grooves in the upper and the lower edges of the cylinder and to provide it with 'O' rings. Instead, I

Fig. 4.2.1

Fig. 4.2.2

chose another way; I put rapid glue on one edge then put the cylinder on some rather thick rubber sheet (the surplus from making a garden pond). Then I cut off the surrounding rubber using a sharp knife and afterwards I cut off the rubber inside the cylinder bore. After that I repeated the process at the other end, and so the cylinder was provided with two rubber seals.

The displacer piston is fitted inside the cylinder. Its thickness is half of the height of the cylinder (i.e. 11 mms) and the diameter is 3 to 4 mms less than the inner diameter of the cylinder (i.e. 86 mms). As the power of the engine is negligible, the piston has to be made of a very light material. Here it is made of styro-foam which came from some packaging material. The centre of the piston is provided with a wooden plug fixed by ordinary paper glue. The purpose of this plug is to make a base for the piston rod. Prick a small hole in the plug and put the piston rod (a short, very thin steel wire) into the hole and fix it with glue.

The piston rod needs a guide bush which fits quite tightly to the rod. A hole was drilled above the centre of the displacer cylinder and onto this the guide bush, which is a leather washer, is glued to the copper plate. It works well but before starting the engine it is important to grease the washer and the piston rod.

The engine frame is a pillar made of Rosewood fastened at its base to a piece of brass. This is adjustable in order to make it possible to move the pillar into the best position above the guide bush mentioned. A hole has been drilled in the pillar 7.5 cms above the base for mounting the shaft of the fly wheel bearing. This bearing and the inner part of the flywheel come from a PC hard disc. The flywheel revolves well because the bearings are small.

As you can see in Fig. 4.2.1 and again in the close up in Fig. 4.2.3, the engine is provided with only one crankpin. That is because the displacer piston works vertically and the power piston works horizontally. In this way the engine meets the demand for an angle of 90 degrees between the displacer piston and the power piston, and no further work is required to achieve this.

The adjustable crankpin has been provided with a little counter weight and two ball bearings for the connecting rods. The ball-bearings have been fitted with copper straps. The strap on the bearing nearest to the fly wheel has then been connected to a little eye in an adjustable Z-shaped steel wire. The other end of this this Z wire (which is similar to the design of model No.1 in chapter 1) is connected to a little eye in the rod of the displacer piston. Perhaps it looks somewhat flappy, and so it is. That's because such a slack construction can help to avoid friction between the individual parts mentioned.

The power cylinder and the power piston are made of glass, cut from a small syringe. The end of the con rod is fixed to a coupling block which is secured inside the piston with a little epoxy repair-sealer. The other end of the con rod is mounted on the crank pin.

Fig. 4.2.3

The diameter of the power piston is 9 mms. It isn't much but nevertheless it is sufficient to make the engine revolve.

The power cylinder is connected to the displacer cylinder by a plastic tube. One of the ends of the tube is connected to the displacer by a brass tube with a soldered collar, which fits a hole drilled in the upper end plate, and is glued to it.

This engine caused many problems. The engine only turned a little and then it stopped. The first thing I did was to make the flywheel (the PC disc) heavier. As this didn't work, I thought that perhaps the flywheel had to be a larger one. I enlarged the flywheel so that the diameter became 14.5 cms. (The larger fly wheel is a cut-off of an old 78 RPM gramophone record.) This was the solution to the problem.

As mentioned earlier, the copper plates had not been made circular. This means that the surface of the lower copper plate (the hot one) is too large and will give off heat. To avoid this the surface has been insulated with a piece of balsa wood. The upper copper plate (the cold one) is provided with cooling fins but mainly as a decoration. The engine, when placed on two mugs filled with boiling water, will run at 90 RPM for 15 minutes. Not bad considering the background. Engines that are better built such as those, for example, fitted with a power piston made of graphite, can revolve for hours at 100 RPM powered only by the heat from the palm of a hand

I observed on my engine that the piston and the cylinder (both in this case being made of glass) need to be very clean. If not, friction arises and the engine doesn't work.

A friend of mine has bought two LTD engines from *American Stirling*. These are shown in Fig. 4.2.4 & 4.2.5 below.

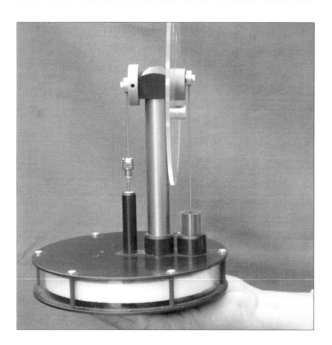

Fig. 4.2.4

This engine is powered only by the heat from the palm of a hand. As the difference in the temperature of the "hot" plate and the "cold" plate is very low, the engine will also run if you place it on ice or cold water. In this case the flywheel turns in the opposite direction.

Fig. 4.2.5

This engine is a *Ringbom* engine in which the displacer rod is not connected to the crank. The diameter of the displacer rod is rather wide so the rod itself works as a piston. The displacer moves up and down as the pressure inside the displacer cylinder varies. On this example the cylinder of the displacer rod is mounted on the lower plate.
Some other LTD engines have a diaphragm, rather than a power piston, connected to a crank or a Ross linkage.

CHAPTER 5

STIRLING ENGINES PAST AND PRESENT

It is to be expected that people discovering Stirling engines for the first time will wonder if they are only toys or whether they can be used, like other engines, to run machinery, provide energy and propel vehicles.

The story of Stirling engines covers almost 200 years, is very involved and, because you can get broader and better explanations in other publications, only an brief outline of its history and development is given here.

If you are fascinated by these wonderful machines, you can read books written by good authors and it is easy, and highly recommended, to get information from websites on the Internet. If you search, for example, under "stirling engine" or "hot air engine" you will be surprised just how many really interesting sites are to be found. Whilst it is by no means an exhaustive list, you will find some recommended reading and websites in the appendix following this chapter.

The Stirling engine is an old engine but the concept is genius; it hasn't gone out of use and still has a future. Developments of the engine are still taking place in many countries at universities and in companies and the use of the Stirling principle has been extended.

As you will have observed, the design of the engine is very simple. It has no valves, it recycles the air and it has external combustion. It is unlike, for example, petrol engines and jet engines which have internal combustion. As a result it can run on almost any kind of fuel, or heat source.

Stirling Engines in the Past

The first era of the Stirling engine was from its invention in 1816 to around the time of the First World War. During that period they were well-known and were used in many ways to provide power.

Some examples include pumping water for cattle at big farms and supplying water to domestic houses; powering machinery in factories and workshops (including running sewing machines) and pumping air for church organs. Smaller ones were used to drive dentists' drills, fans in hot countries, popcorn machines, gramophones and so on.

Compared with steam engines they were safer as Stirling engines have no boiler, and those of this period did not involve high pressures, they could started quite quickly and they didn't need a full-time engineer to take care of the engine.

As with any form of engine, the Stirling engine cannot produce more power than is put into it by heat. For most of this first era, the Stirling engine's only competitor was the steam engine, in which heat is used to turn water to steam under pressure, and it is the very considerable expansion of the high pressure steam which gives the steam engine its power. In the Stirling engine there is no boiler, water or steam, just air being alternately heated and expanded, and cooled and contracted, to provide power.

In theory applying more heat to larger engines should have resulted in more power, and this was tried with at least one steam beam engine being converted to a hot air engine, and the Swedish American engineer and inventor Ericsson actually built an ocean liner powered by a giant, twin cylinder Stirling engine.

Neither of these experiments was successful, partially for mechanical reasons - the extra weight of the parts absorbed too much of the increased power, but primarily because, at that time, the metals used often couldn't withstand the amount of heat required, and the hot end of the displacer cylinder burned out. This was before Bessemer steel and stainless steel became widely used.

However, during this period many improvements did take place and many engines of different sizes and designs were built for commercial use where their low power output was not a problem, or when the fact they could be left running unattended for long periods was an advantage - Pumps being the best example of this.

Far and away the most important of these improvements was the Regenerator. This is a very important part of a Stirling engine if you want to obtain high efficiency and it is important to note that when Robert Stirling (as far as I know) applied for a Scottish patent in 1816, the invention was described as a vessel for recycling heat in glass factories, breweries and distilleries to diminish the consumption of fuel. Even though the engine was of great importance it was, in a way, a supplementary part of the application.

The function of the regenerator is to receive heat when the air from the hot end of the cylinder passes by to the cold end; to store that heat, and release it when the air again passes by to the hot end. The effect was to make an engine much more efficient as the

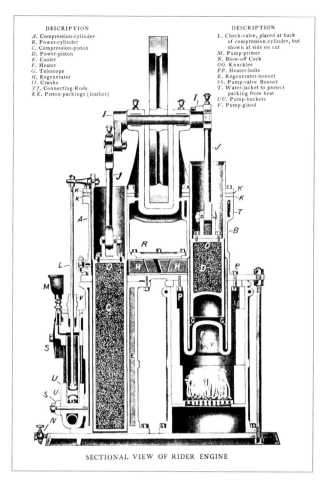

DESCRIPTION
A. Compression-cylinder
B. Power-cylinder
C. Compression-piston
D. Power-piston
E. Cooler
F. Heater
G. Telescope
H. Regenerator
II. Cranks
JJ. Connecting-Rods
KK. Piston-packings (leather)

DESCRIPTION
L. Check-valve, placed at back of compression-cylinder, but shown at side on cut
M. Pump-primer
N. Blow-off Cock
OO. Knuckles
PP. Heater-bolts
R. Regenerator-bonnet
SS. Pump-valve Bonnet
T. Water-jacket to protect packing from heat
UU. Pump-buckets
V. Pump-gland

SECTIONAL VIEW OF RIDER ENGINE

Fig. 5.1.1

This is a Rider engine, manufactured by the *Rider-Ericsson Engine Co.* in the U.S.A. It works on the Stirling principle but it is an "Alfa configuration". In this configuration it is the power cylinder 'D' which is heated while the other (displacer) cylinder 'C', fitted with a water cooler, takes care of compression and cooling the air. The connection between the two cylinders is provided with metal fins which constitute the regenerator 'H'.

heating/cooling cycle was speeded up.

The regenerator can be mounted inside or outside the displacer cylinder and it can be made of thin metal plates or webs or steel wool. Fig. 5.1.1 shows a section through an engine fitted with a regenerator.

Both this engine, and that shown in Fig. 5.1.2, were used for pumping water and were available in various sizes. The largest version of the Rider engine had a 10" cylinder and stood 7'9" to the top of the fly-wheel. It could pump around 3,500 gallons per hour running at 110 revolutions per

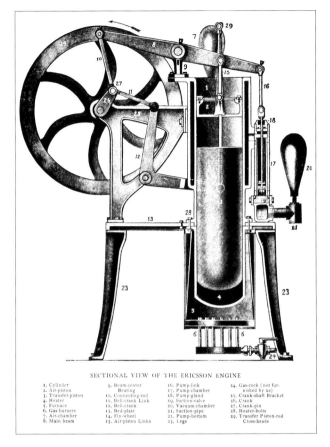

SECTIONAL VIEW OF THE ERICSSON ENGINE

1. Cylinder	9. Beam-center	16. Pump-link	24. Gas-cock (not fur-
2. Air-piston	Bearing	17. Pump-chamber	nished by us)
3. Transfer-piston	10. Connecting-rod	18. Pump-gland	25. Crank-shaft Bracket
4. Heater	11. Bell-crank Link	19. Suction-valve	26. Crank
5. Furnace	12. Bell-crank	20. Vacuum-chamber	27. Crank-pin
6. Gas-burners	13. Bed-plate	21. Suction-pipe	28. Heater-bolts
7. Air-chamber	14. Fly-wheel	22. Pump-bottom	29. Transfer Piston-rod
8. Main beam	15. Air-piston Links	23. Legs	Cross-heads

Fig. 5.1.2

This engine has a "Beta" configuration. As described earlier, these engines have a single cylinder which contains both the power piston '2' and displacer '3'. The Ericsson engines does not have a specific regenerator, but the very large displacer piston would would have partially acted as one. In both the Rider and the Ericsson engines there was a constant flow of water through the cooling jackets, which formed part of the pump circuit.

minute, and pump this up to a vertical height of 350 feet. It could be heated by coal, wood or kerosene, weighed 3,700 pounds packed for shipping and, in 1906, cost $540.00.

This was the most efficient engine built by the Rider-Ericsson Engine Co., but they also sold considerable numbers of a smaller, less complex and less efficient engine which was also much cheaper, the Ericsson shown in Fig. 5.1.2.

The largest of this type of engine also had a 10" cylinder but was only 5' 6" in height. The RPM are not stated in the Rider-Ericsson Co's catalogue, but it could pump 1,000

gallons per hour to a vertical height of 160 feet. Whilst its performance was not as good as the Rider type, at 1,700 pounds, it weighed less than half of that, and cost only $300.00 which may explain its success, especially in remote country areas.

The British Robinson engine, a 'Gamma' configuration, was also well-known. It had an interesting drive linkage but the engine wasn't very efficient because of a rather large dead-space inside the engine. In the bottom and at the top of the displacer piston, holes were drilled to allow air to pass through the piston instead of being transferred around it because the piston was fitted inside with annular metal plates making up a regenerator. A cross-section of the engine is shown in Fig. 5.1.3.

Stirling engines like the Rider, the Ericsson and the Robinson, and many other makes, were sold in their thousands and were effective at doing the work for which they were designed. But even in these roles the type was doomed by the arrival in the late nineteenth century of the internal combustion engine and electricity, and use of the Stirling engine largely died out in the

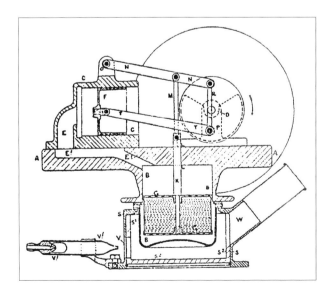

Fig. 5.1.3

A Robinson engine

early twentieth century, other than as a toy and in very specific uses such as powering fans where electricity was not available. It is probably true to say that, at this time, the virtues of the Stirling engine - its potential mechanical efficiency, silence and ability to run on many fuels, were appreciated, but further development was needed to realise these virtues; meanwhile the internal combustion engine and the electric motor gave similar benefits, and were readily available.

5.2 The revival of the Stirling engine

In the mid nineteen-thirties, *Philips* of Eindhoven, Holland, were looking for an engine to drive a generator to make electricity to power radio transmitters and radio sets in remote places.

There were some requirements the engine had to fulfil; it should be reliable, have no spark plug to cause interference with the radio signals, be noiseless and not smell, and should also be able to run on different kinds of fuel.

After many investigations the Stirling engine was chosen and thus began a new era with various experiments, inventions and patents being taken out. *Philips* spent a huge amount of money over many years; the project continued, largely in secret, during World War II only coming to an end in the 1970s, and many good results were achieved. Those are still of importance to the ongoing development of the Stirling engine today.

It is a very long story, but important developments that can be mentioned are: (1) the use of helium under pressure in place of atmospheric air, (2) the speed of the engines was increased to five thousand RPM., (3) the seals of the system were

Fig. 5.2.1
A Philips Type 102c Generator Set
Photograph courtesy of Andy Ross

greatly improved, (4) drive mechanisms, the Rombic Drive for instance, were invented and developed at that time and (5) modern materials capable of resisting the heat and pressure stresses were used.

In Fig. 5.2.1, a Philips Stirling engine generator set, type 102c, from the beginning of the nineteen-fifties, is shown. It worked well and was noiseless.

Commercial interest in the Stirling engine was increased further by its ability to be used as a cooling engine. It is remarkable and of importance to mention here that if you let another engine drive a Stirling engine, the displacer cylinder grows cold at one end and hot at the other. It does make not just a small difference between the temperatures mentioned, but a very large difference, and nowadays Stirling engines are also used to create very low temperatures such as that used for cryocooling.

Philips has also, in association with *DAF* automobiles, tried to make engines for buses but in this instance there were still problems with the materials of the heated part of the engine. *General Motors* and *Ford* in the U.S.A. were also interested in this line of development and obtained licences to make engines for automobiles and military equipment as well as other developments. Whilst one bus, and at least one car powered by a Stirling engine resulted, it is believed that these projects have been halted. The major reason for this is that a high power Stirling engine is a very advanced piece of technology and, in the present circumstances, there is no call to invest huge sums of money in bringing it to commercial production. In this particular case, the environmental benefits of using a Stirling engine are likely to be met more cheaply by using either electric power on its own, or a combination of electric and I.C. power in H.E.V. (Hybrid Electrical Vehicle) vehicles.

The efforts by *Philips* didn't really succeed either. There were many reasons for this but, apart from the invention of the transistor which changed the former need for electric power, other products took up most of the company's resources; it was a time when, for example, most Europeans were buying TV sets and *Philips* became leaders in providing these. In the nineteen-seventies *Philips* stopped working on Stirling engine development, as it was found to be unjustifiable economically, but all Stirling engine enthusiasts owe the company a debt of gratitude for reawakening interest in this type of engine.

(The whole story of the Philips Stirling engine development programme is told in the book "The Philips Stirling Engine" by C.M. Hargreaves, published by Elsvier; this is currently out of print, but should be available through a good library).

5.3 Stirling Engines Today

A few modern uses of the Stirling engine are mentioned here, but the internet will again provide many interesting and very informative websites.

Nowadays, Stirling engines are being used for many purposes within the obvious areas of use for conventional engines, and some are now being used in new ways.

Let us begin with energy production, both in small and large applications.

In co-operation with the New Zealand based company *Whisper Tech*, the Dutch company, *Victron Energy*, has developed a different version of a modern Stirling engine. It has four cylinders and is a comparatively small engine, but it is efficient and can provide a large sailing boat or a remote house with heat and electricity. The engine is a *CHP* (Combined Heat and Power) plant.

The engine's dimensions are 65 x 45 x 50 cms and the weight is 90 kg. The exhaust gases are clean and the noise level is as low as 44 db because of the continuous combustion process. The engine is equipped with a microprocessor which controls all the functions.

The consumption of the diesel fuel used to provide the heat is 0.8 litre per hour at full load, and the engine produces 1,600 Ah/12 V or 800 Ah/24 V over a 24 hour period. This corresponds to the energy requirements of a detached house or a big sailing boat with 8 people on board. The system gas is nitrogen rather than helium or air.

The batteries act mainly as a buffer, rather than for storage, and in size and weight are around fifty per cent less than would be required in a system where the generator is not on continuously. Routine maintenance is restricted to cleaning the evaporator every 2,000 running hours (three months continuous operation) and the "Whisper Gen" has been designed to give 20,000 running hours before needing an overhaul. The waste heat from the burner is recovered via a heat exchanger and, as a result, 90% 0f the energy in the fuel is turned into usable power or heat. A picture of the engine, and diagrams of it in marine and domestic use, is shown in Fig. 5.3.1. *(My thanks to Victron Energy for this information)*

This is a lot of facts about just one engine but the information is necessary just to get an idea of the concept of a modern Stirling engine. It will also, perhaps, explain the background of some of the rather small, external plants, often fuelled with biomass, which can, for example, be used to provide a village with heat and power.

In the nineteen-sixties Professor William T. Beale of Athens, Ohio, invented the Free Piston Stirling engine. This engine has a power piston and a displacer provided with a piston, but no crank, the pistons being moved by the changing of the pressure inside the engine. The piston rods are mounted on special springs which allow

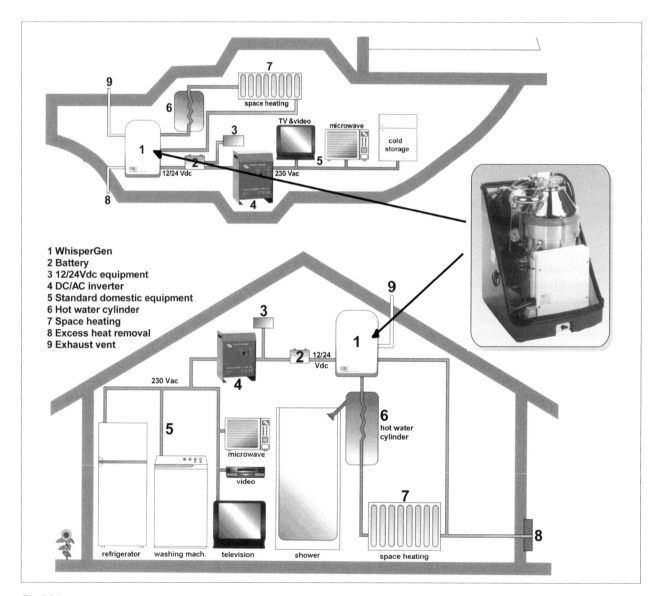

Fig. 5.3.1
Layouts of the WhisperGen in both marine and domestic use
Reproduced courtesy of Victron Energy

the pistons to vibrate. One of the best ways to get power out of these engines is to provide them with an alternating generator.

Many years ago Prof. Beale started his own company, *Sunpower*, which has established a considerable reputation for advising both large companies and governments on the potential of the Stirling engine.

The free piston engine is very promising and if, instead of heating the engine, you supply it with alternating electricity this will change the engine into a brilliant cooling machine. In some designs this might be as a cryocooling machine and in others simply to lower temperatures - in refrigerators, for example. It is possible that

this linear compressor will replace the present compressors; *Sunpower* report that a large Korean company, *LG Electronics*, is making refrigerators incorporating the *Sunpower* linear compressor. Fig. 5.3.2 shows a free piston engine of a design developed by *NASA* for use, for example, in space satellites.

Stirling engines are also used for military purposes such as cooling infrared detectors and generating energy. In space technology the engines are used for cooling electronic equipment and making electricity on board space stations.

Now let us look at an application of the Stirling engine on an altogether larger scale.

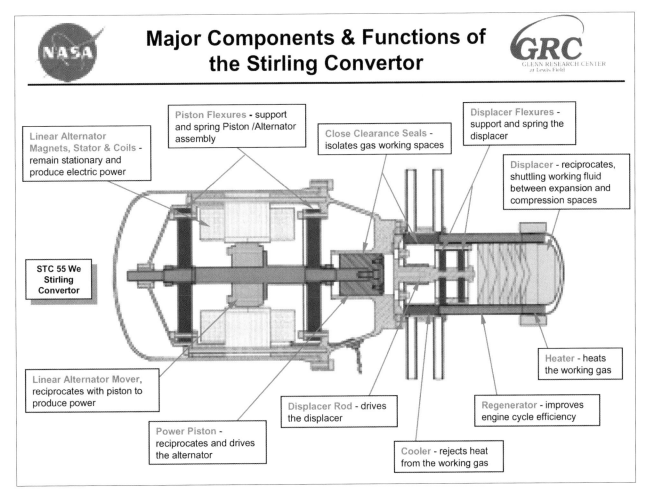

Fig. 5.3.2
Layout and parts of a Free Piston Engine

Reproduced courtesy of NASA

Submarines often need to remain submerged for long periods, running on electrical power when nuclear energy is not acceptable or possible. A problem arises when the batteries need recharging, as it is necessary for the submarine to surface and use its diesel engine to do this. However a Stirling engine can be the solution and the Swedish company, *Kockums*, has designed and developed an air independent propulsion system (AIP) and some submarines, in the Swedish, Danish and Australian Navies are now equipped with such AIP Stirling engines. These are not used to replace the main diesel engine but to generate electricity for the main engine propelling the vessel when it is submerged for a long time. The Stirling engine is heated by burning pure oxygen and diesel fuel, in a pressurised combustion chamber in this instance, and the length of time the vessel can remain submerged is primarily dictated by the amount of stored liquid oxygen. Figs. 5.3.3, 5.3.4 & 5.3.5 illustrate this system.

Combining Solar Energy and Stirling engines is not a new idea. John Ericsson made experiments in a small scale in 1870

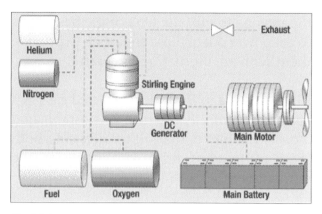

Fig. 5.3.4.
Diagrammatic layout of the Kockums Stirling AIP system
Diagram courtesy of Kockums

by using a parabolic mirror to heat the hot end of the displacer. Nowadays quite large Dish Stirling Systems are installed in locations where there is considerable sunshine, such as California and Spain.

It is planned to make large Stirling Dish Parks in desert areas such as Arizona for example. At night, or when the sun isn't shining, the engines needed can be run the using gas or oil. Fig. 5.3.6 shows a picture of a Stirling Dish System built by *SES* (Stirling Energy System).

From these details it will be clear that the Stirling engine has been developed to a point where it can develop real power, and is currently being used for a whole range of applications. As it is low emission by nature, the Stirling engine must surely have a place in our more environmentally conscious world; it should also be of use in helping the Third World to provide power, and pump water, using local fuels.

Robert Stirling (1790 - 1878) was not an engineer but a minister in the Church of Scotland. He was conscientious in the care of his parish and was highly respected and promoted inside the church. He was interested in technology from a young age, and this interest was reinforced by his studies at university. He was twenty six

Fig. 5.3.3
A Kockums Stirling AIP system engine installed in a submarine.
Photograph courtesy of Kockums

Fig. 5.3.5
The Kockums Stirling AIP system installed in a submarine.

Layout reproduced courtesy of Kockums

years old when he applied for his first patent. Along with his brother, James Stirling, who was ten years his junior and had qualified as a civil engineer, he went on to obtain patents relating to hot air engines and both of them became well-known and respected in technical circles.

Now, nearly two hundred years after Robert Stirling developed his engine, it continues in use. It is very difficult to predict further improvements of the engine, and its prospects for the future, but the Stirling engine will surely both survive, and find uses in many new areas.

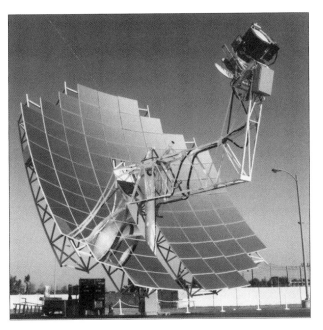

Fig. 5.3.6
A Stirling Dish System with a Kockums Stirling' engine.

Photograph courtesy of Stirling Energy System

Robert Stirling's first regenerative air engine, based on his patent application of 1816

CHAPTER 6

HOW A STIRLING ENGINE WORKS

The Stirling cycle is described here using photographs of a demonstration model. This layout is a Beta configuration (one cylinder and two pistons), like Robert Stirling's first engine.

In Fig. 7.1, the displacer piston is at the left and is a loose fit to the cylinder so that air can be transferred around it. The piston on the right is the power piston which is a slip fit to the cylinder, as in a steam engine.

The displacer piston rod passes through the power piston and joins a connecting rod which is connected to a crank pin. The power piston rod joins another connecting rod which is connected to another crank pin on the same crankshaft. A flywheel (not shown) is fitted on the crankshaft.

Heat is applied at the Hot End on the left and the cylinder is cooled, by air or water, at the Cool End.

In Fig. 7.1 the displacer is situated close to the hot end of the cylinder, the power piston is near the limit of its travel at the cool end of the cylinder, and most of the air in the cylinder is located at the cool end.

If the crank is tuned a quarter clock-wise,

the displacer piston will move a little to the right and then back; this is only a short movement as its crank pin was close to its top position. However the power piston makes a much greater movement to the left and compresses the air inside the cylinder. This position is shown in Fig. 7.2

The result of turning the crank a further quarter turn is shown in Fig. 7.3 where it is the displacer piston which has made the major movement, to the right, displacing the air in the cool end past it to the hot end, where the air is now heated and expanded. The power piston only moves a little back and forth as this happens.

The heated and expanded air flows round the displacer piston and drives the power piston to the right, turning the crank and the flywheel. The position after this has happened is shown in Fig. 7. 4.

During a further quarter turn of the crank the power piston makes a minor movement, but the displacer piston makes a long movement to the left, transferring the hot air round it to the cool end, where it contracts, pulling the power piston to the left and bringing us back to Fig. 7.1 again.

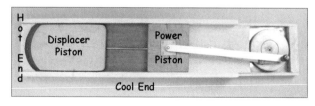

Fig. 7.1

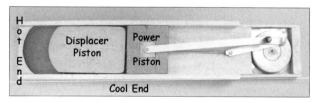

Fig. 7.3

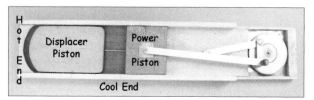

Fig. 7.2

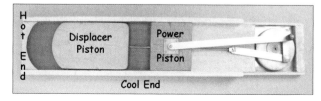

Fig. 7.4

APPENDIX: USEFUL BOOK, VIDEOS AND WEBSITES

The books and websites mentioned here are only a small selection of sources of information and only books I have read myself are listed below.
The websites shown are the results of test searches.

BOOKS:

Robert Sier:
Hot Air Caloric and Stirling Engines Vol. 1 (331 pages L.A. Mair).*
Describes hot air engines from the very beginning up to the present day. It is very well illustrated with pictures and drawings.

Robert Sier:
Rev Robert Stirling D.D. (189 pages, L.A. Mair).*
This book is a biography but it also includes drawings, technical information and Robert Stirling's further developments of his engine.

Andy Ross:
Stirling Cycle Engines (122 pages, Solar Engines).
Tells the story of the Stirling engine and the developments of the engines. The book is well illustrated.

James G. Rizzo:
The Stirling Engine Manual Vol. 1 (183 pages, Camden Miniature Steam Services).*
This book gives a lot of information about Stirling engines and their history, but is mainly addressed at people who want to build hot air model engines. The book is well illustrated including drawings of models and contains a great deal of useful advice.

James R. Senft:
An Introduction to Stirling Engines (80 pages, Moriya Press).*
Covers the physics and explains how the engine works. It is well illustrated and will teach you a lot about Stirling engines.

James R. Senft:
An Introduction to Low Temperature Differential Stirling Engines (88 pages, Moriya Press).*
James R. Senft gives a lot of information about of this fascinating engine. It includes many illustrations and there are also drawings for building an engine yourself.

Finkelstein & Organ:
Air Engines (261 pages, Professional Engineering Publishing).*
This book gives broad information about the engines and their history but at the same time the book, written by two leading authorities on Stirling engines, covers the subject in depth and goes into a lot of technical detail.

VIDEOS:

Robert Bailey:
An Introduction to Hot Air Engines (80 minutes, available in NTSC format from Bob Bailey or in PAL format from Camden).
Bob Bailey is a well-known name in the world of Stirling engines in U.S.A.. In this video he shows how Stirling engines work, demonstrates models, visits model builders and great shows with old restored engines.

Periscope Productions NV:
The Stirling Experiment (53 minutes). The video begins with some background and continues with interviews with, amongst others, Robert Sier, James R. Senft, C.M. Hargreaves, some of the people who were involved with the Philips development programme, manufacturers of Stirling engines and a naval officer speaking of the Kockums Stirling.

Items marked * are available from Camden Miniature Steam Services (www.camdenmin.co.uk) who also stock many other titles on hot air engines

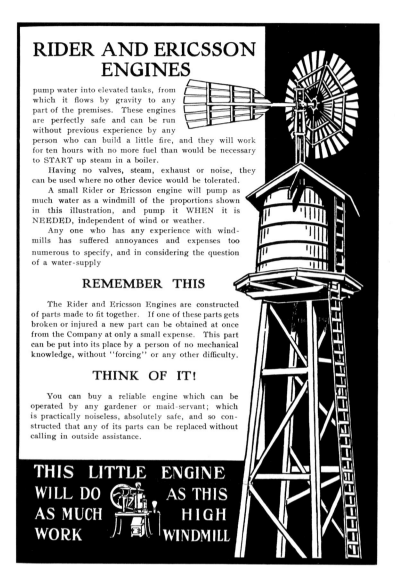

RIDER AND ERICSSON ENGINES

pump water into elevated tanks, from which it flows by gravity to any part of the premises. These engines are perfectly safe and can be run without previous experience by any person who can build a little fire, and they will work for ten hours with no more fuel than would be necessary to START up steam in a boiler.

Having no valves, steam, exhaust or noise, they can be used where no other device would be tolerated.

A small Rider or Ericsson engine will pump as much water as a windmill of the proportions shown in this illustration, and pump it WHEN it is NEEDED, independent of wind or weather.

Any one who has any experience with windmills has suffered annoyances and expenses too numerous to specify, and in considering the question of a water-supply

REMEMBER THIS

The Rider and Ericsson Engines are constructed of parts made to fit together. If one of these parts gets broken or injured a new part can be obtained at once from the Company at only a small expense. This part can be put into its place by a person of no mechanical knowledge, without "forcing" or any other difficulty.

THINK OF IT!

You can buy a reliable engine which can be operated by any gardener or maid-servant; which is practically noiseless, absolutely safe, and so constructed that any of its parts can be replaced without calling in outside assistance.

THIS LITTLE ENGINE WILL DO AS MUCH WORK AS THIS HIGH WINDMILL

WEBSITES:

The Stirling Engine Society:
www.stirlingengines.org.uk

American Stirling Company:
www.stirlingengine.com

Keveney:
www.keveney.com

NASA:
www.grc.nasa.gov

Quiet Revolution Motor Co.:
www.qrmc.com

Robert Bailey
www.baileycraft.com

Sunpower:
www.sunpower.com

Whisper Tech:
www.whispertech.co.nz

Victron Energy:
www.victronenergie.nl

SOLO Kleinmotoren:
www.stirling-engine.de

Solar Engines/PM Reasearch:
www.pmresearchinc.com

Sandia:
www.sandia.gov

Stirling Energy System:
www.stirlingenergy.com

Kockums, Shipyard:
www.kockums.se